This Donut Date Journal
Belongs To:

_____

The Disciple Making Parent's

Donut Date Journal

70 Questions to Connect You
to Your Child's Heart

Chap Bettis

DIAMOND HILL
PUBLISHING

THE DISCIPLE-MAKING PARENT'S DONUT DATE JOURNAL: 70 Questions to Connect You to Your Child's Heart
Copyright © 2017 by Chap Bettis.
Diamond Hill Publishing
All rights reserved.
ISBN-13:978-0999041000
ISBN-10:0999041002

For more information or to order in bulk visit www.donutdatejournal.com.

Cover and interior design by Jeff Flynn
www.jflycreative.com

Table of Contents

Part 1: Laying the Foundation

Part 2: Questions and Answers

Part 3: Extras

PART 1

LAYING THE FOUNDATION

1

Understanding the Power of Donut Dates

Do you remember what it was like to hold your newborn for the very first time? God gave a precious and fragile gift—to you! Do you remember how unprepared you felt?

But then the parenting journey began. And before you knew it, activities started to pull you in a thousand different directions. Should we take them to dance? Music lessons? Baseball or soccer practice? And on and on the list goes. Life seemed so simple when your child was so young. You spent hours just watching her play and grow.

In the midst of all this external activity, you also know your child is changing on the inside. At least, you know it theoretically. As our children grow older it takes effort to have real heart-to-heart communication with them. Good activities can crowd out deep conversation. Life that started out as a leisurely rafting trip down the river of parenting has turned into constant rapids. You are barely hanging onto the raft.

The Common Trap

It is not at all unusual for parents to fall into this common trap. We can allow the urgent to crowd out the important. Each activity seems important at the moment, but together, they have crowded out the important work of heart connection.

The good news is that it does not have to be that way. In the Scriptures, a fruit of the gospel is turning the hearts of parents and children back to each other (Malachi 4:6, Luke 1:17).

You can establish and maintain a strong heart connection with your children as young children, tweens, teenagers, and even into their 20s. But that heart connection does not happen automatically. It comes from deliberate communication and commitment. Intentional time provides the space to walk through the ups and downs of life. Time to communicate allows us to talk through the normal tensions in a parent–child relationship. Often our disagreements and anger come because we are starved for communication time.

Even families who are successfully navigating the rapids of activities and enjoying quality family time will benefit from this communication habit.

Staying Connected and Making Relational Deposits

As a busy pastor, I was well aware of all the demands that could have led me to ignore my children; and I certainly did not want that to happen. After we had four children two years apart (think: 6, 4, 2, newborn), our home was pretty crazy. How was I going to stay connected to my children in the midst of pastoral demands?

I am hesitant to prescribe certain activities for becoming a disciple-making parent. I know too well my own pharisaical, list-making heart that doesn't look for God's work, rather my own "to-do" list. Nevertheless, we all need specific suggestions. So allow me to heartily recommend taking your children out for Donut Dates (or muffin dates or breakfast dates or pizza dates). Just a few hours will pay off huge dividends.

I don't remember when this tradition started in our family. But on a regular basis, I would take one of my four children out before school to a local donut shop. That one-on-one date allowed me to focus on one individual child for at least a moment. (Too often parenting four children two years apart felt like herding cats!). In addition, it allowed them to have my undivided attention to talk about anything they wanted to. We were going somewhere special just for me to focus on getting to know them!

I would bring along a small notebook and record answers to the questions I asked. The notebook was a visual record of their answers throughout the years. In addition, writing down their answers was a visible indication that what they had to say was important.

We carried this tradition on not just with our young children but with our teens as well. I've observed that right when our teens need us to listen to them and ask questions the most, parents have a tendency to back off. Taking one teen out at a time enabled us to have a calm conversation about a topic. It also allowed me to ask questions to discover what challenges they were facing. Because of all the relational deposits, the dates gave us a context to have some more difficult conversations. I can remember several "come-to-Jesus" talks I had with my teenage sons. Previous positive breakfasts made a corrective time possible.

Finally, creating this relational "space" also allowed me to reveal my heart. As the children grew into their teen years, there were times I had to ask their forgiveness. Other times I asked them to pray for certain challenges I was facing. Our relationships grew in depth and complexity as they grew older.

A Letter from My Daughter

To encourage you in the benefits of Donut Dates, consider this recent letter from my twenty-two-year-old daughter:

> *I can remember clearly the excitement of my eight-year-old self when it was my turn to go out with Dad. Every few weeks we would drive to a donut shop right down the road. Not only did I get to stuff my mouth with colorful sprinkles and strawberry milk, but I got Dad all to myself.*
>
> *He would ask questions like who my best friends were or what my favorite subject in school was. All my answers were written down in a maroon journal that was just for my dates with Dad. This was a sweet and cherished tradition that carried on for many years.*

Even as a teenager, I stayed close and connected with my dad. The questions he asked were more serious and self-reflective. Now, as a college senior, I recognize the trusting and loving communication these special dates fostered. Although I don't go to that donut shop with Dad anymore, I still love talking with him in his office when I visit from college.

Looking back, these times showed me how a man should treat a woman and the importance of asking intentional questions to grow a relationship. My dad's undivided attention over a small donut was a simple act that grew a little girl's heart.

To all the dads, moms, and grandparents who are reading this, you hold a book of questions that can grow a young heart closer to you just like this heart did.

Practical Suggestions

To close this introduction, let me make several suggestions.

Keep your eye on the goal. The ultimate goal is to create heart connection with your son or daughter. It is to make relational deposits so they feel free to tell you anything. You are seeking to provide space in the busyness of life to connect with them.

Don't feel like you have to take them out every week. With four young children and a busy pastoring schedule that included other breakfast meetings, I tried to have a Donut Date regularly, though it might be six weeks between dates with each particular child. Sometimes we would go several weeks without a date at all; but I didn't even have to keep track, because they certainly knew whose turn it was to go out for a donut!

Think long term. Just put this into your routine and pick a cycle you can sustain. Go somewhere inexpensive. The benefit comes not in a quick blast of activity that then falls off but by sustaining the date over many years. That's what helped make the emotional impact.

Ask good questions. If you are really interested in them, then go prepared with questions. It is not just the donuts but the asking to know them that connected our hearts. For me, writing down the answers in a journal was vitally important. I wanted to create a keepsake, and I wanted them to know that I cared about their answers. Of course, as they grew older, I didn't write down every answer. It just became a time to talk.

Listen well. This suggestion is related to asking good questions. The next section has a chapter from *The Disciple-Making Parent*. In it, we think about how our God is a listening God. By contrast, our sin fights against us listening to others. Often we stay quiet, just waiting for our turn to talk. That's not really hearing their heart. Study your children and listen to them. Learn to ask good follow-up questions. Often the follow-up questions are just as important as the initial question. A probing "Tell me more about that" is very encouraging. Remember, the greatest communication skill is learning to listen well. God wants to make us more Christ-like by making us better listeners.

Put down your phone. This was not a distraction in my day, but it certainly is today. In fact, a common complaint of *children* is that their parents are on the phone all the time. My heart drops when I am out for breakfast and see a dad with his child on a date constantly checking his phone. I wonder if he's aware of the message he is sending to his child.

Make sure your children feel your affection. You're taking them out not because you have to, but because you want to. This is a powerful time for them to feel your love. And your best plan for that outcome is to put away the distracting thoughts you have and really focus on them.

Go 1-to-1. There is certainly a place for a parent to take all the children out for a fun event. However, that will not accomplish the purpose at which we are aiming. It will not create that special heart connection between one adult and one of your children. Deep heart things will not be shared in a group of siblings.

Start before you need to. It's never too early! (Well ok, taking a newborn out is a little silly, but you know what I mean.) You want to start before you sense a distance in the relationship. You are training your children to trust and communicate with you.

Having said that, it's also never too late! If you are the parent of a teen whose heart has grown distant, go out anyway, full of love. Practice open-ended questions. Prepare to love them unconditionally through their non-communication. The questions for older children might be especially helpful for you.

How to Use this Book

With those practical exhortations in hand, let me introduce you to the rest of the book.

Chapter Two is an excerpt from my book, *The Disciple-Making Parent*. This chapter expands on the call to grow in communication with your children. Read it carefully. *The purposes of a [child's] heart are deep waters but a [parent] of understanding draws them out (Proverbs 20:5 with my modifications)*. Grow deeply in this area of skillful shepherding of your child.

In the bulk of the book I list 70 questions I have collected. I have given you room to write down your children's answers several times over the years. Be sure to include the date you write down the answer. You'll find the questions arranged from the simple, appropriate for young children, to those more appropriate for older children. After the 70 questions, you will find pages to add your own favorite questions.

In the final part of the journal I included a fun place to record the details of your child's birth. Each story is unique in the challenges that you were facing and the events that transpired around them. Our family would often retell the story on that child's birthday. But over time the events become... fuzzy. So take it from an older father and write them down!

In addition, there is a place to record memorable events in your child's life. And on the last page there are some suggested questions for asking teens that might not be appropriate to journal.

If you are start-
ing out with
young children
who love the idea,
then take the book
along on your date
and record the answers.
As you read in the letter
from my daughter, she
was looking forward to the
event. Put it on your calen-
dar and make a big deal of it.

If you are starting with a child or
teen you're feeling distant from,
you might want to communicate
the idea of a date in a more low-key
way. Perhaps just suggest you go out
for breakfast to "catch up on what's
been happening." Go to that time with
planned questions and then record the
answers when you get home.

Conclusion

Our lives are changed by the conversations we have. We would do
well to be intentional about many of those conversations. Build-
ing in the space, time, and affection for those conversations will
bear much fruit later on in life.

Who are your closest friends right now?
What do you like about them?

Date: 3/4/2015   At Dunkin
I love Jenny. We play dolls
together. Monica always makes me
laugh when our families get together.
I love playing superheroes with her
Date: 5/15/2017   Panera Bread
Makenna moved to Texas. I'll
miss swimming in her pool and
playing stuffed animals wit

Date:

Date:

Those Donut Dates provided huge relational dividends for the amount of money and time I invested and continue to invest. I cannot recommend a format like this highly enough. I am confident the Lord will bless the individual time you give your children.

2

KEEPING YOUR HEARTS CONNECTED BY SKILLFUL COMMUNICATION

—Excerpt from *The Disciple-Making Parent*

My dear brothers take note of this: Everyone should be quick to listen, slow to speak, and slow to become angry. (James 1:19 NIV)

Melinda's request rocked her parents. She hadn't given them outward signs of rebellion. She seemed pretty well-adjusted at the school for missionaries' kids. But now—this. She wanted a belly button piercing!

How would you handle that situation? Shock? Anger? A mocking laugh, followed by a loud, "No!"? Wailing and gnashing of teeth? Or would you just shrug your shoulders? And what would you decide? What would you say to Melinda?

Most important for our purposes is not the specific decision the three of them made, but how they made it. A decade later I asked her, "What do you think your parents did well in passing the gospel baton to you?" She immediately related this story to me and then paid this compliment to her parents: "My parents always talked through things with me. I felt like I could tell them what was on my mind. We either talked through an issue until they changed their mind or until I felt heard."

Time and time again, I hear a similar theme from young people walking with the Lord. They describe parents who were approachable and who would not react. They looked for the biblical principle in the situation and dug deeper for heart motivation.

Disciple-making parents make heart communication a priority.

Good Communication Needs Time

Our lives are changed by the conversations we have. Intentional discipleship involves intentional conversations. By the time my children leave home we will have had thousands of conversations. Some will be life changing for good. Or they might change our relationship for the worse. How will those conversations have taken place? Will those conversations be intentional, prayerful, and skillful? Or will they be haphazard, fleshly, and piercing?

Heart connection takes time. The gospels record many intentional conversations Jesus had with his disciples—and this does not even include the hours of conversation the group would have had as they walked from village to village. Paul also gave individual attention when he ministered:

For you know how, like a father with his children, we exhorted each one of you and encouraged you and charged you to walk in a manner worthy of God, who calls you into his own kingdom and glory. (1 Thessalonians 2:11-12)

When it comes to discipling our children, times of intentional, individual conversation can be life changing. But what types of conversation should I look for? If I study the life of Jesus, I see that he had times of intentional conversation and times of spontaneous conversation.

Intentional Time – Breakfast

I have tried regularly to take my children out for a breakfast. Even though I don't look forward to smelling like grease the rest of the day, it's a small price to pay for connecting to their hearts. Breakfast with just one child slows me down, allows me to focus on that individual, to listen intently to him or her, and to share what is on my heart. In fact, it has probably given the biggest relational returns for the amount of money and time invested.

Looking in my journal recently, I found a comment I recorded when one of my daughters was fourteen. She related to me "Dad, I love going out to breakfast with you. It helps me feel connected to you." That's exactly what we've been talking about—heart connection!

Intentional Time – Jonathan Edwards

Puritan theologian and pastor Jonathan Edwards never took his children out for donuts; but he did take time to communicate with them intentionally. Samuel Hopkins observed Edwards' attention and affection during the afternoon:

> *Entering freely into the feelings and concerns of his children and relaxing into cheerful and animate conversation accompanied frequently with sprightly remarks and sallies of wit and humor...then he went back to his study for more work before dinner.*[1]

Through this observation, we see a serious man engaging his family with joy on a regular basis. In addition, Edwards took time to individually shepherd the heart:

> *The Edwards made it a point to single out individual children from the humming family hive, to get to know each one in turn by himself.*[2]

> *Samuel Hopkins observed, "He took opportunity to converse with them singly and particularly about their...Soul's Concern."*[3]

And lest we object that Edwards could take this time because he was a pastor, his biographers note that he rose before it was light and would often study into the night. We find time to do that which we value. A wise parent will make time for intentional, individual conversation.

Other Intentional Times

Intentional communication should change as our children change. When our children were younger, Sharon made it a habit to tuck them into bed. She used that time for listening and drawing out their hearts. Her habit of asking them about their day or if anything was bothering them led to many fruitful conversations. This changed when these same children were teenagers and their bedtimes were later than mine! But we still sought to keep our hearts connected. Other families seek to keep the connection in different ways. Where the desire to connect is in place, God will give us a method that fits our situation and personality.

The Power of Spontaneous Communication

When we look to the ministry of Jesus, we also see another type of communication—spontaneous communication. Jesus often taught his disciples spontaneously. The disciples would make a comment that revealed their hearts, and Jesus would impress some truth. Or another person would interact with him, and then Jesus would turn to his disciples and teach them. Learning was occurring as life presented itself.

Likewise, there are crucial times when our children open a window into the depths of their hearts. They are ready to talk. Perhaps they are wrestling with worrisome thoughts, or maybe they have faced a painful time. Their deeper thoughts have bubbled over. As parents, we need to stop, look, and listen. This is a divine moment. Your child, an eternal soul, is opening his or her heart and entrusting you with his deepest thoughts. What will you do? Don't trample this moment. Your children are looking to see if they can trust you. One wise mom I know so values these moments, that she will put off housework and chores to have these conversations. To use her words, housework and chores are "catch-up-able;" this window into their hearts is not.

Quick to Listen

Convinced of the need to keep our hearts connected in either a planned or spontaneous way, what is the number-one communication skill we should focus on? Surprisingly, it has nothing to do with speaking but everything to do with listening.

Tedd Tripp explains:

> *The finest art of communication is not learning how to express your thoughts. It is learning how to draw out the thoughts of another. Your objective in communication must be to understand your child, not simply to have your children understand you. Many parents never learn these skills. They never discover how to help their children articulate their own thoughts and feelings.*[4]

As God the Spirit matures you as a communicator, he wants to grow you in the ability to really listen and understand. Our God listens to his people. The reason we have planned times of communication with our children is not to dump information on them but to draw them out.

James 1:19 nicely summarizes three communication goals for all of us—parents and children. We are commanded to be quick to listen, slow to speak, and slow to become angry.

Listen Well

When James tells us to be quick to listen, he repeats a theme of Proverbs:

> *If one gives an answer before he hears, it is his folly and shame. (Proverbs 18:13)*

> *A fool takes no pleasure in understanding, but only in expressing his opinion. (Proverbs 18:2)*

Many times I have been foolish when I have not listened to my child. I "mind-read." I speak before I listen. I subconsciously think, "I don't need to hear you out. I already know what you are thinking." God calls this foolishness!

Take this quick test:

- **Do I listen when they want to talk?** Do I love them enough to interrupt my agenda? Or do I half listen while thinking about something else?

- **Do I maintain good eye contact?** Eye contact creates connection. Am I smiling at them and expressing affirmation?

- **Am I giving them my focused attention?** Or am I distracted by other things like my phone or computer?

- **Do I interrupt them?** Do I "read their mind?" Or am I asking questions to understand them better?

Training Our Children to Listen

Rightly, in the previous section, we have emphasized really listening to the heart of our children. But there needs to be a corresponding corrective. Just as parents can be guilty of over talking, so can our children. Their natural self-centeredness often causes them to talk when they should listen. Proverbs is filled with warnings about talking too much.[5] Part of training our children in godliness is training them to listen. A child expresses honor to his or her parents and to those who are older by listening. After the Father placed his blessing of endorsement on Jesus, he commanded, "Listen to him" (Matthew 17:5). Why? Because sinful people are prone not to listen to those we should.

Even as I listen to my children, every thought of theirs does not have to be expressed. There is a good and right time for them to submit by listening to us. And it is our job as parents to skillfully shepherd them in this way. Jesus, at twelve, was listening to the teachers and asking questions (Luke 2:46). Disciple your children to become good listeners. Shepherd them out of their natural self-centered over talking. Train them to ask questions and listen to those who are older and wiser. We treasure our beautiful young children by delighting in them and by training them to exercise self-control with their speech.

Using Good Questions

When James says we are to be slow to speak, he is not talking about the speed of our words. He is talking about our quick jump to giving answers. Scripture provides a powerful word picture to keep us from rushing to conclusions:

> *The purpose in a man's heart is like deep water, but a man of understanding will draw it out. (Proverbs 20:5)*

Proverbs 20:5 suggests what we already know, that there are different levels of communication (see Figure to right)[6] Below cliché, which is just surface conversation, real communication begins at the level of information. Most of our conversation with our children is at this second level. We find out how they did on a test at school or what time their soccer game is. This is the easiest level to have a conversation. The third level represents opinions. Here we start to find out what they think about different things. The next, deeper level is their feelings; and even deeper is their transparency level Communication happens at all these different levels. Remember, a parent of understanding draws out those deeper levels. And God gives us questions to draw out the deep waters of a child's heart.

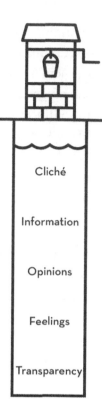

Questioning Well

Some people collect baseball cards, comic books, or even cars. I like to collect questions. (Strange, I know!) The right question can open up a conversation. A quick study of the life of Jesus reveals that he often used questions as a discipleship tool.

The following are some questions that might be of use to you as you shepherd your children and probe the deeper waters.

Questions to Open Up Communication

Open-ended questions invite communication. They allow our children to set the agenda.

- What are some challenges you are facing?
- What are you thinking about these days?
- What's the best thing that happened today? What was the worst?

Questions to Dig Deeper

Once our children have started a conversation, we can continue to ask questions to understand more deeply.

- What has influenced you to think this way?
- Help me understand what you were thinking at the time.
- Why do you think that? Can you explain that to me?

Questions to Clarify Communication

Sometimes miscommunication happens because we do not understand the other person. Clarifying questions help. It can be helpful to repeat what they just said.

- This is what I have heard you say. Is that correct?
- Have I understood you?

Questions to Provoke Their Understanding

Jesus often employed questions to move the disciples' understanding to the next level.

- What do you think Jesus thinks (and God's Word

says) about…?

- What verses speak to this situation?
- Looking back, what do you think you should have done differently?
- What will you do the next time this happens?

Questions to Open Up Spiritual Conversations
- How can I pray for you?
- Where are you reading in the Word these days?
- What has God been teaching you lately?

Questions to Ask to Restore the Relationship
A well-placed question can help lower the wall between two people at odds.

- How do you think I have sinned against you? How do you think you sinned?

Questions to Prepare Them for an Event
Asking what our children would do in a hypothetical event prepares them and makes them articulate their response.

- What would you do if…?
- What would you say if someone asked you…?

Having a desire to listen and ask skillful questions can open up your child's heart. Start your own list of favorite questions. Become a student of your child.

In all these questions, we must have a humility of spirit. Unlike

Jesus, we do not know what is in a person's heart. Don't be like the lawyer who asks prosecuting questions to attack the person. Questions should come from a loving, inquiring heart.

Conclusion

Melinda's parents heard her heart motivations. They prayed about her request. They talked her through different concerns. But ultimately, they decided to let her have the piercing. Today it is not an issue. Melinda is a campus worker with a national college ministry. Both she and her parents reference that time as formative in Melinda's walk with the Lord. Looking back, what was important was not what they decided but how they decided it.

In this chapter we have focused on listening well. But there comes a time when we need to care for the heart by speaking. We will turn our attention to speaking well in the next chapter.

Disciple-making parents make heart communication a priority.

---

1. Elisabeth D. Dodds, *Marriage to a Difficult Man*
(Laurel, MS: Audubon Press, 2004), 50.

2. Ibid., 54.

3. Douglas A. Sweeney, *Jonathan Edwards and the Ministry of the Word*
(Downers Grove, IL: InterVarsity, 2009), 64.

4. Tedd Tripp, *Shepherding a Child's Heart*
(Wapwallopen, PA: Shepherd Press, 2005), 72-73.

5. See Proverbs 10:8, 10:10, 10:19, 17:27.

6. This popular insight can be found many places including the handbook for "A Weekend to Remember" (Family Life, 2009), 26.

PART 2

QUESTIONS AND ANSWERS

Write your signature.

Date: _____ _____

_____

Date: _____ _____

_____

Date: _____ _____

_____

Date: _____ _____

_____

Date: _____ _____

_____

What is your favorite stuffed animal?

Date: _____ _____

_____

_____

_____

_____

Date: _____ _____

_____

_____

_____

_____

Date: _____ _____

_____

_____

_____

_____

Date: _____ _____

_____

_____

_____

_____

Who are your closest friends right now? What do you like about them?

Date: _____ _____

_____

_____

_____

Date: _____ _____

_____

_____

_____

Date: _____ _____

_____

_____

_____

Date: _____ _____

_____

_____

_____

What is your favorite food?

Date: _____ _____

_____

_____

_____

_____

Date: _____ _____

_____

_____

_____

_____

Date: _____ _____

_____

_____

_____

_____

Date: _____ _____

_____

_____

_____

_____

What is your favorite joke?
Tell it to me.

Date: _____ _____

_____

_____

_____

_____

Date: _____ _____

_____

_____

_____

_____

Date: _____ _____

_____

_____

_____

_____

Date: _____ _____

_____

_____

_____

_____

What is your favorite time of year? Why?

Date: _____ _____

_____

_____

_____

_____

Date: _____ _____

_____

_____

_____

_____

Date: _____ _____

_____

_____

_____

_____

Date: _____ _____

_____

_____

_____

_____

What is your favorite color?

Date: _____ _____

_____

_____

_____

_____

Date: _____ _____

_____

_____

_____

_____

Date: _____ _____

_____

_____

_____

_____

Date: _____ _____

_____

_____

_____

_____

What is your favorite birthday party memory from your last birthday?

Date: _____ _____

_____

_____

_____

_____

Date: _____ _____

_____

_____

_____

_____

Date: _____ _____

_____

_____

_____

_____

Date: _____ _____

_____

_____

_____

_____

What is your favorite song?

Date: _____ _____

_____

_____

_____

_____

Date: _____ _____

_____

_____

_____

_____

Date: _____ _____

_____

_____

_____

_____

Date: _____ _____

_____

_____

_____

_____

What are you looking forward to?

Date: _____ _____

_____

_____

_____

_____

Date: _____ _____

_____

_____

_____

_____

Date: _____ _____

_____

_____

_____

_____

Date: _____ _____

_____

_____

_____

_____

What do you like best
about _____ (our pet)?

Date: _____ _____

_____

_____

_____

_____

Date: _____ _____

_____

_____

_____

_____

Date: _____ _____

_____

_____

_____

_____

Date: _____ _____

_____

_____

_____

_____

What is one question we could ask your grandparents to find out about their childhoods?

Date: _____ _____

_____

_____

_____

_____

Date: _____ _____

_____

_____

_____

_____

Date: _____ _____

_____

_____

_____

_____

Date: _____ _____

_____

_____

_____

_____

What makes you unique?
Describe yourself in five words.

Date: _____ _____

_____

_____

_____

_____

Date: _____ _____

_____

_____

_____

_____

Date: _____ _____

_____

_____

_____

_____

Date: _____ _____

_____

_____

_____

_____

What book are you reading right now?

Date: _____ _____

_____

_____

_____

_____

Date: _____ _____

_____

_____

_____

_____

Date: _____ _____

_____

_____

_____

_____

Date: _____ _____

_____

_____

_____

_____

Suppose you could make yourself invisible. What would you do?

Date: _____ _____

_____

_____

_____

_____

Date: _____ _____

_____

_____

_____

_____

Date: _____ _____

_____

_____

_____

_____

Date: _____ _____

_____

_____

_____

_____

If you could be an animal, what would you be? Why?

Date: _____ _____

_____

_____

_____

_____

Date: _____ _____

_____

_____

_____

_____

Date: _____ _____

_____

_____

_____

_____

Date: _____ _____

_____

_____

_____

_____

Who is the funniest person in your life? Why are they funny?

Date: _____ _____

_____

_____

_____

_____

Date: _____ _____

_____

_____

_____

_____

Date: _____ _____

_____

_____

_____

_____

Date: _____ _____

_____

_____

_____

_____

What is your favorite movie?
What do you like best about it?

Date: _____ _____

_____

_____

_____

Date: _____ _____

_____

_____

_____

Date: _____ _____

_____

_____

_____

Date: _____ _____

_____

_____

_____

What is your favorite band/artist?
Why do you like them?

Date: _____ _____

_____

_____

_____

_____

Date: _____ _____

_____

_____

_____

_____

Date: _____ _____

_____

_____

_____

_____

Date: _____ _____

_____

_____

_____

_____

What is your favorite video game?
What do you like best about it?

Date: _____ _____

_____

_____

_____

_____

Date: _____ _____

_____

_____

_____

_____

Date: _____ _____

_____

_____

_____

_____

Date: _____ _____

_____

_____

_____

_____

What is your favorite vacation memory from the past year?

Date: _____ _____

_____

_____

_____

_____

Date: _____ _____

_____

_____

_____

_____

Date: _____ _____

_____

_____

_____

_____

Date: _____ _____

_____

_____

_____

_____

What is your favorite school memory from this past year?

Date: _____

_____

_____

_____

_____

Date: _____

_____

_____

_____

_____

Date: _____

_____

_____

_____

_____

Date: _____

_____

_____

_____

_____

Who is your favorite athlete/celebrity? What is it that you admire about them?

Date: _____ _____

_____

_____

_____

_____

Date: _____ _____

_____

_____

_____

_____

Date: _____ _____

_____

_____

_____

_____

Date: _____ _____

_____

_____

_____

_____

What do you like most about your mom/dad? How can we tell her/him?

Date: _____ _____

_____

_____

_____

_____

Date: _____ _____

_____

_____

_____

_____

Date: _____ _____

_____

_____

_____

_____

Date: _____ _____

_____

_____

_____

_____

What are you some things you are thankful for? Let's come up with five.

Date: _____ _____

_____

_____

_____

Date: _____ _____

_____

_____

_____

Date: _____ _____

_____

_____

_____

Date: _____ _____

_____

_____

_____

What was something fun you did this week?

Date: _____ _____

_____

_____

_____

_____

Date: _____ _____

_____

_____

_____

_____

Date: _____ _____

_____

_____

_____

_____

Date: _____ _____

_____

_____

_____

_____

What is your favorite subject in school? Why?

Date: _____ _____

_____

_____

_____

_____

Date: _____ _____

_____

_____

_____

_____

Date: _____ _____

_____

_____

_____

_____

Date: _____ _____

_____

_____

_____

_____

What is the hardest thing in school right now? Why?

Date: _____ _____

_____

_____

_____

_____

Date: _____ _____

_____

_____

_____

_____

Date: _____ _____

_____

_____

_____

_____

Date: _____ _____

_____

_____

_____

_____

Who is your favorite teacher?
What do you like about him or her?

Date: _____ _____

_____

_____

_____

_____

Date: _____ _____

_____

_____

_____

_____

Date: _____ _____

_____

_____

_____

_____

Date: _____ _____

_____

_____

_____

_____

What food that we eat do you dislike?

Date: _____ _____

_____

_____

_____

Date: _____ _____

_____

_____

_____

Date: _____ _____

_____

_____

_____

Date: _____ _____

_____

_____

_____

What is the biggest challenge you are facing?

Date: _____ _____

_____

_____

_____

_____

Date: _____ _____

_____

_____

_____

_____

Date: _____ _____

_____

_____

_____

_____

Date: _____ _____

_____

_____

_____

_____

Do you remember the last dream you had? What was it about?

Date: _____ _____

_____

_____

_____

_____

Date: _____ _____

_____

_____

_____

_____

Date: _____ _____

_____

_____

_____

_____

Date: _____ _____

_____

_____

_____

_____

What makes a good friend?
Do you think you are good at those things?

Date: _____ _____

_____

_____

_____

_____

Date: _____ _____

_____

_____

_____

_____

Date: _____ _____

_____

_____

_____

_____

Date: _____ _____

_____

_____

_____

_____

If you could have three wishes, what would they be?

Date: _____ _____

_____

_____

_____

Date: _____ _____

_____

_____

_____

Date: _____ _____

_____

_____

_____

Date: _____ _____

_____

_____

_____

If you could change one thing about our family, what would it be?

Date: _____ _____

_____

_____

_____

_____

Date: _____ _____

_____

_____

_____

_____

Date: _____ _____

_____

_____

_____

_____

Date: _____ _____

_____

_____

_____

_____

What do you want to be when you grow up?

Date: _____ _____

_____

_____

_____

_____

Date: _____ _____

_____

_____

_____

_____

Date: _____ _____

_____

_____

_____

_____

Date: _____ _____

_____

_____

_____

_____

What do you love most about your brothers and sisters?

Date: _____ _____

_____

_____

_____

Date: _____ _____

_____

_____

_____

Date: _____ _____

_____

_____

_____

Date: _____ _____

_____

_____

_____

If you could go anywhere in the world on vacation, where would you go?

Date: _____ _____

_____

_____

_____

_____

Date: _____ _____

_____

_____

_____

_____

Date: _____ _____

_____

_____

_____

_____

Date: _____ _____

_____

_____

_____

_____

If you could go back in time, where would you go?

Date: _____ _____

_____

_____

_____

_____

Date: _____ _____

_____

_____

_____

_____

Date: _____ _____

_____

_____

_____

_____

Date: _____ _____

_____

_____

_____

_____

What's your biggest accomplishment so far?

Date: _____ _____

_____

_____

_____

_____

Date: _____ _____

_____

_____

_____

_____

Date: _____ _____

_____

_____

_____

_____

Date: _____ _____

_____

_____

_____

_____

What are you saving money for? Why?

Date: _____ _____

_____

_____

_____

_____

Date: _____ _____

_____

_____

_____

_____

Date: _____ _____

_____

_____

_____

_____

Date: _____ _____

_____

_____

_____

_____

Who do you want to know better?
How can we make it happen?

Date: _____ _____

_____

_____

_____

_____

Date: _____ _____

_____

_____

_____

_____

Date: _____ _____

_____

_____

_____

_____

Date: _____ _____

_____

_____

_____

_____

What was your favorite
Christmas present this past year?

Date: _____ _____

_____

_____

_____

_____

Date: _____ _____

_____

_____

_____

_____

Date: _____ _____

_____

_____

_____

_____

Date: _____ _____

_____

_____

_____

_____

If you could change anything about your room, what would it be?

Date: _____ _____

_____

_____

_____

_____

Date: _____ _____

_____

_____

_____

_____

Date: _____ _____

_____

_____

_____

_____

Date: _____ _____

_____

_____

_____

_____

If you could go back three years and give advice to yourself, what would you say?

Date: _____ _____

_____

_____

_____

_____

Date: _____ _____

_____

_____

_____

_____

Date: _____ _____

_____

_____

_____

_____

Date: _____ _____

_____

_____

_____

_____

What are you learning that might be helpful as an adult?

Date: _____ _____

_____

_____

_____

_____

Date: _____ _____

_____

_____

_____

_____

Date: _____ _____

_____

_____

_____

_____

Date: _____ _____

_____

_____

_____

_____

Who is someone you admire in our church? Why?

Date: _____ _____

_____

_____

_____

_____

Date: _____ _____

_____

_____

_____

_____

Date: _____ _____

_____

_____

_____

_____

Date: _____ _____

_____

_____

_____

_____

What makes you laugh?

Date: _____ _____

_____

_____

_____

_____

Date: _____ _____

_____

_____

_____

_____

Date: _____ _____

_____

_____

_____

_____

Date: _____ _____

_____

_____

_____

_____

What is one question you would like to ask your mom/dad?

Date: _____ _____

_____

_____

_____

_____

Date: _____ _____

_____

_____

_____

_____

Date: _____ _____

_____

_____

_____

_____

Date: _____ _____

_____

_____

_____

_____

What is something fun you are looking forward to?

Date: _____ _____
_____
_____
_____
_____

Date: _____ _____
_____
_____
_____
_____

Date: _____ _____
_____
_____
_____
_____

Date: _____ _____
_____
_____
_____
_____

What is the hardest thing about being a kid?

Date: _____ _____

_____

_____

_____

_____

Date: _____ _____

_____

_____

_____

_____

Date: _____ _____

_____

_____

_____

_____

Date: _____ _____

_____

_____

_____

_____

What is something you had to do that you didn't like doing?

Date: _____ _____

_____

_____

_____

_____

Date: _____ _____

_____

_____

_____

_____

Date: _____ _____

_____

_____

_____

_____

Date: _____ _____

_____

_____

_____

_____

What do you think few people understand about you?

Date: _____ _____

_____

_____

_____

Date: _____ _____

_____

_____

_____

Date: _____ _____

_____

_____

_____

Date: _____ _____

_____

_____

_____

Where have you seen God at work in your life?

Date: _____ _____

_____

_____

_____

_____

Date: _____ _____

_____

_____

_____

_____

Date: _____ _____

_____

_____

_____

_____

Date: _____ _____

_____

_____

_____

_____

What is your favorite Bible story? Why?

Date: _____ _____

_____

_____

_____

_____

Date: _____ _____

_____

_____

_____

_____

Date: _____ _____

_____

_____

_____

_____

Date: _____ _____

_____

_____

_____

_____

Who was the last person to make you upset? Why?

Date: _____ _____

_____

_____

_____

_____

Date: _____ _____

_____

_____

_____

_____

Date: _____ _____

_____

_____

_____

_____

Date: _____ _____

_____

_____

_____

_____

Who in our family do you feel closest to?
What do you like about them?

Date: _____ _____

_____

_____

_____

_____

Date: _____ _____

_____

_____

_____

_____

Date: _____ _____

_____

_____

_____

_____

Date: _____ _____

_____

_____

_____

_____

What is one question you have about your faith?

Date: _____ _____

_____

_____

_____

Date: _____ _____

_____

_____

_____

Date: _____ _____

_____

_____

_____

Date: _____ _____

_____

_____

_____

Is anything making you anxious or nervous? What?

Date: _____ _____

_____

_____

_____

_____

Date: _____ _____

_____

_____

_____

_____

Date: _____ _____

_____

_____

_____

_____

Date: _____ _____

_____

_____

_____

_____

What is one challenge you have that I could help you with?

Date: _____ _____

_____

_____

_____

_____

Date: _____ _____

_____

_____

_____

_____

Date: _____ _____

_____

_____

_____

_____

Date: _____ _____

_____

_____

_____

_____

If you could change one thing about yourself, what would it be?

Date: _____ _____

_____

_____

_____

_____

Date: _____ _____

_____

_____

_____

_____

Date: _____ _____

_____

_____

_____

_____

Date: _____ _____

_____

_____

_____

_____

What would you like me to pray for?

Date: _____ _____

_____

_____

_____

_____

Date: _____ _____

_____

_____

_____

_____

Date: _____ _____

_____

_____

_____

_____

Date: _____ _____

_____

_____

_____

_____

What do you want to remember from this time of your life?

Date: _____ _____

_____

_____

_____

_____

Date: _____ _____

_____

_____

_____

_____

Date: _____ _____

_____

_____

_____

_____

Date: _____ _____

_____

_____

_____

_____

On a scale of 1 to 10, how was your week? Why?

Date: _____ _____

_____

_____

_____

_____

Date: _____ _____

_____

_____

_____

_____

Date: _____ _____

_____

_____

_____

_____

Date: _____ _____

_____

_____

_____

_____

Is there anyone we need to tell about Jesus? How can we?

Date: _____ _____

_____

_____

_____

_____

Date: _____ _____

_____

_____

_____

_____

Date: _____ _____

_____

_____

_____

_____

Date: _____ _____

_____

_____

_____

_____

What are you looking for in a guy? Girl?

Date: _____ _____

_____

_____

_____

_____

Date: _____ _____

_____

_____

_____

_____

Date: _____ _____

_____

_____

_____

_____

Date: _____ _____

_____

_____

_____

_____

Where do you think you will be in five years? What do you think it will be like?

Date: _____ _____

_____

_____

_____

_____

Date: _____ _____

_____

_____

_____

_____

Date: _____ _____

_____

_____

_____

_____

Date: _____ _____

_____

_____

_____

_____

Who do you want to be like when you grow up? Why?

Date: _____ _____

_____

_____

_____

_____

Date: _____ _____

_____

_____

_____

_____

Date: _____ _____

_____

_____

_____

_____

Date: _____ _____

_____

_____

_____

_____

What is the last verse you memorized?

Date: _____ _____

_____

_____

_____

_____

Date: _____ _____

_____

_____

_____

_____

Date: _____ _____

_____

_____

_____

_____

Date: _____ _____

_____

_____

_____

_____

What is a life lesson you have learned recently that you want to remember?

Date: _____ _____

_____

_____

_____

_____

Date: _____ _____

_____

_____

_____

_____

Date: _____ _____

_____

_____

_____

_____

Date: _____ _____

_____

_____

_____

_____

Write your own question here.

Date: _____ _____

_____ _____

_____

_____

_____

Date: _____ _____

_____

_____

_____

_____

Date: _____ _____

_____

_____

_____

_____

Date: _____ _____

_____

_____

_____

_____

Write your own question here.

Date: _____ _____

_____

_____

_____

_____

Date: _____ _____

_____

_____

_____

_____

Date: _____ _____

_____

_____

_____

_____

Date: _____ _____

_____

_____

_____

_____

Write your own question here.

Date: _____ _____

_____

_____

_____

_____

Date: _____ _____

_____

_____

_____

_____

Date: _____ _____

_____

_____

_____

_____

Date: _____ _____

_____

_____

_____

_____

Write your own question here.

Date: _____ _____

_____

_____

_____

_____

Date: _____ _____

_____

_____

_____

_____

Date: _____ _____

_____

_____

_____

_____

Date: _____ _____

_____

_____

_____

_____

Part 3

Extras

THE DAY YOU WERE BORN

Children love to hear the story of their birth. One good time to retell that story is on your child's birthday. Unfortunately, over time, the details can start to become hazy. Take some time to write down the events and details of that special day.

_____

_____

_____

_____

_____

_____

_____

_____

_____

_____

_____

_____

_____

_____

_____

MEMORABLE DATES

This page is a place to record memorable dates in your child's spiritual walk. It may be the day they received Christ, were baptized, or talked with someone about Jesus. It may be other significant dates in their academic or life journey.

MORE QUESTIONS TO ASK

As your children grow older, you will want to ask them even deeper heart connecting questions. The purpose would not be to record your answers but to connect with the heart. The following are some suggestions:

1. Is there anybody you need to ask forgiveness of?

2. Have you ever wanted to give up on something?

3. If you could change one thing about our family, what would it be?

4. Is there any way you feel I have sinned against you or need to ask forgiveness of you?

5. Have you ever felt like hurting yourself?

6. If you could ask God for anything what would it be?

7. How can I pray for you?

Use the following space to record other questions that prompt deeper conversations with your older children.

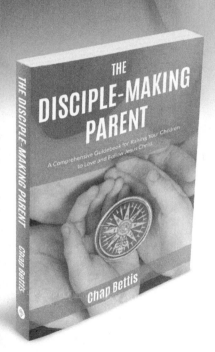

Made in the USA
Middletown, DE
03 May 2024